MADE BY GARRETTS

An Introduction to the Products of Leiston Works

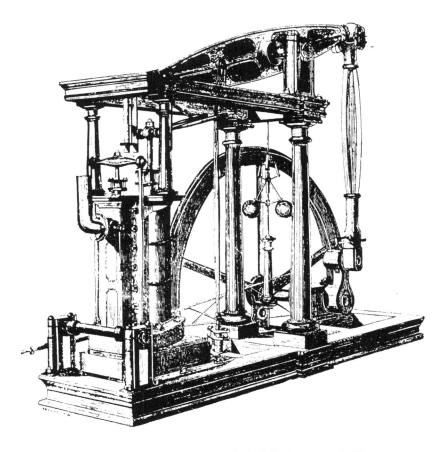

R.A. Whitehead & Partners
Tonbridge, Kent

1994

Acknowledgements.

The idea for this book came from David Williamson of the Long Shop Museum, and I am grateful to the Trustees and Friends of the Museum for their support.

By courtesy of Richard Garrett Engineering Ltd. I was allowed to have copies made of the Works collection of pictures, a task most ably undertaken by Barry J. Finch. Unless otherwise acknowledged this is the source of illustrations.

Robert A. Whitehead

Cover: *Garrett* Suffolk Punch *(No.33180) built in 1919, and now in the collection of the Long Shop Museum, Leiston.* *[Photograph:* Ben R. Cronin*]*
Title Page: *A beam engine of the 1850's*

Photographs are from the author's collection except where otherwise acknowledged.

Typeset in Arial 8 by J.E.Whitehead.

Printed and bound by Biddles Ltd., Woodbridge Park, Guildford GU1 1DA

Published by R.A.Whitehead & Partners, 42, Hadlow Road, Tonbridge, Kent TN9 1NZ

ISBN 0-9508298-4-6

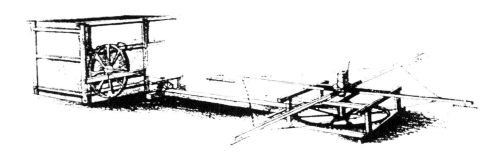

The machine that started the firm on the road to fame -
a thresher of the type patented by John Balls in 1805, complete with its horsework.

THE FAMILY and THE WORKS

The firm of Richard Garrett & Sons Ltd. dated its beginnings from the year 1778 when the first Richard Garrett of Leiston took over the forge there, already a going concern. He married a Leiston girl, Elizabeth Newson, and their eldest son, named Richard after his father, took over the forge in 1805. It was the second Richard's marriage to Sarah Balls of Hethersett, Norwich, that laid the foundations of machine making at Leiston, for her father, who came into the firm, was John Balls, designer and patentee of the improved threshing machine seen above.

Their son, the third Richard, took the firm on to international fame. Born in 1807, he entered the firm in 1821, took over its finances when only nineteen, and was in total control by the age of 29. Soon afterwards he began the making of fixed steam engines and much more developed threshing machines. The firm went on, in 1848, to build portable steam engines, had a large stand at the Great Exhibition in Hyde Park in 1851, and in 1858 made one of its portables capable of propelling itself along the road. From then on it was not long before traction engines were made, at first, under licence, to the designs of Thomas Aveling, but soon to the firm's own design. A great variety of agricultural and general machines were also made; horse hoes, seed drills, ploughs, horse rakes, reaping machines, sawbenches, machines for making drainage tiles, and so on.

Richard III had four sons enter the firm, Richard IV, John, Henry, and Frank. John and Henry found they could not agree with their brothers and took themselves off to other spheres - John to start a similar works in Magdeburg, Germany, and Henry to a fullers' earth mine near Bath. After Richard III died in 1866, Richard IV and Frank continued as partners until the former died in 1884, whereafter Frank was sole principal until joined by his eldest son, also Frank, in 1890, and later by his other sons, Alfred, Stephen, and Victor. The firm became a limited company in 1897.

From then until 1918 was a period of continuous expansion. Building traction engines, which had lapsed for a decade, was resumed, and the building of steam rollers, road locomotives, steam tractors, and steam wagons was taken up as well as an enhanced output of portable engines and large self-contained steam power plants. At its peak the Works had a staff of 2000. Frank Garrett (Senior) died in 1918 and was succeeded as head of the firm by his eldest son. Stephen, the third son, had been killed at Neuve Chapelle in 1915 and his place on the board was filled by his younger brother, Victor.

At the time of the Russian revolution the firm had large sums of money owing to it in Russia, a debt repudiated by the new Soviet Government, and this loss weakened its finances. In 1919 the new chairman and his friend, Thomas Aveling, first proposed and then set up a combine called Agricultural & General Engineers Ltd. to incorporate several of the important firms in the industry (listed on page 27). An indifferent management structure and poor trading conditions, however, made it a weak organisation which succumbed to the slump early in 1932.

After a spell in Receivership the Works was taken over in July, 1932, by Beyer Peacock & Co.Ltd. of Manchester, builders of railway locomotives, who formed a new company, Richard Garrett Engineering Works Ltd. (latterly shortened to Richard Garrett Engineering Ltd.). Beyer Peacock themselves fell on difficult times in the 1960's, and after a number of changes of ownership, Leiston Works was finally closed in 1979.

Below: *Leiston Works after the Long Shop was built in 1853. The railway locomotive on the Works line just inside the gate is artist's licence - all traffic was then worked by horses.*

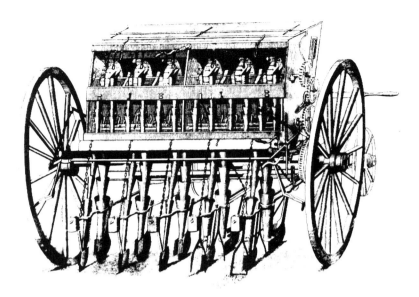

A Suffolk seed-drill c.1851

AGRICULTURAL MACHINES

The earliest activities of the Works seem to have been the making of edge tools, mostly sickles (an example of which is on display in the Long Shop), and general smiths' work. After Richard II's father-in-law, John Balls, joined the firm it seems that the making of his patent thresher (Patent No.2819 of 1805) established the manufacture of agricultural machines. A poster of 1828 showing the products made includes the thresher, ploughs, field rollers, horse hoes, seed drills, chaff cutters, root pulpers, and hay tedders, as well as elaborate iron park gates,and domestic grates and fireplaces.

Threshers and seed drills gradually became the dominant machines though not to the exclusion of others. Many threshers and barn machines were driven by a *horse-work* whereby horses walking in a circle were harnessed to poles fixed at the centre to a vertical shaft from which a system of bevel gears and a drive shaft with universal joints transmitted the power to the driven machine. All early threshers were fixed but the first portable thresher appeared in 1849, and thereafter this pattern rapidly displaced the fixed type. Threshers, of varying sizes, were made in large numbers during the second half of the last century, many being exported to southern and eastern Europe, and to North Africa, and some to South America, and elsewhere. Making seed drills continued but declined in numbers until it ceased early in the 1914-18 war.

Most of the trade with Europe was lost because of that war and the political changes that followed it, but some threshers continued to be sold in North Africa and at home, and development continued. The last design of thresher made by the old company was a steel machine similar to American practice. Hand and power operated mealie shellers were built, and portable decorticators were designed and built for use on sisal plantations. After Beyer Peacock took over these were discontinued though a few threshers were made from parts in stock and for a short while the Middleton Cotton Gin was built. In the 1930's a start was made on building machines for harvesting peat, and after the second war these were made up to 1959, several hundred going to Ireland.

A Hussey-type reaping
machine built by Garretts
c.1851

A fixed thresher of
the 1840's

Norwegian harrow –
late 1840's

No.21437 (1898) - a 6 NHP fixed engine

STATIONARY & PORTABLE ENGINES

It is not known when the Works built its first stationary engine. None is shown on its 1828 poster, but production may have begun soon afterwards. The types made varied from small single cylindered horizontal engines to large beam engines, but the firm also made crank-overhead vertical engines and table engines, in which the crank was in the bottom of a cast iron entablature or 'table' on top of which the cylinder was placed. Later, in the 1880's and 90's, steam winding engines were made for pile driving rigs or shaft sinking, together with a series of horizontal double cylinder engines for the oilfields of South Russia.

None of these were made in large numbers. In the case of the portable steam engine, first made in 1848, however, the Works soon became world-famous. The portable was, in its essentials, a small steam engine on a locomotive type boiler, mounted on travelling wheels, provided with a front lock for steering to which horse shafts were attached for moving it from place to place. A flywheel enabled it to drive a wide variety of machines by endless belt. These portables accompanied most of the threshing machines sold in Europe in the last century, and in the early days of portable threshing machines a number were sold in this country with these engines as the power unit, though once traction engines became available they soon displaced portables here.

In Victorian and Edwardian days the portable engine became the universal provider of transportable power. It was used on construction sites for driving pumps, mortar mills and mixers, in quarries for working crushers, in sawmills for powering saws and planers, in brickyards for turning pugmills, and in joiners' and other workshops for driving overhead line shafting. In fact there can have been few types of moderate sized machines capable of operation by an endless belt that were not, at one time or another, paired up with portables. On farms they could be used to drive an almost infinite variety of machines - a number were supplied for driving so-called 'roundabout ploughing tackle'. Early milking machines took their power from portables as did the first crop driers; the fans of hop oasts; cream separators and butter churns; cake crushers; chaff cutters; root pulpers; and, in at least one case, a cider apple crusher. For very dusty situations such as quarries, Garretts eventually offered portables with the engine parts enclosed in a dustproof cover, but these were never very popular.

The Garrett portable of the 1870's and 80's - a type built at first on wooden wheels, but later on iron wheels

In 1909 production began of a series of large fixed self-contained power plants, either singles or compounds (see under Glossary) based on a corrugated tubular horizontal firebox entirely within the boiler shell and with firetubes from the firebox to the smokebox. The largest of these were capable of delivering 270 b.h.p. - the largest size of portable engine gave 80 b.h.p. The sales of these virtually ceased with the long Coal Strike in 1926. Rural electricity supplies and motor tractors between them halted sales of ordinary portables.

Below: *Layout of a 135 BHP power plant with a 90 Kw. dynamo at a paper mill. The engine is fitted with a down take flue to an existing brick chimney.*

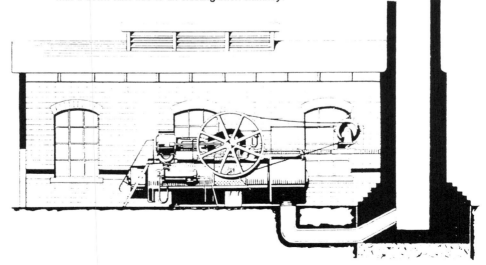

'Locomotion', *the first wholly Garrett self-moving engine, 1858.*

TRACTION ENGINES

At Chelmsford Royal Show in 1856 James Boydell exhibited one of the track-laying engines of his invention, the enginework of which had been built at Leiston. The Garretts did not persist in this type of machine but, instead, in 1858 built a self-moving portable in which the engine could be joined to the rear wheels by chain. Developments of this idea were made until 1875. The firm next turned to making, under licence, chain driven true traction engines to the design of Thomas Aveling of Rochester. These were made in limited numbers until 1871. After a period in which only self-moving portables were offered, in 1876 the firm began to build its own design of gear driven traction engine. Sales of these were disappointing and their manufacture was stopped in 1879 as the great agricultural depression began to bite, though the last one was not sold until 1881. Traction engine building was not resumed until 1895 though in 1887 a solitary chain engine had been made under sub-contract to Thomas Cooper of Great Ryburgh. Once restarted traction engine building continued until 1931, and the final example (No.35461) is in preservation.

Between 1899 and 1905 a series of 8 and 10 NHP vertical drum ploughing engines were built for the firm of Rudolph Sack of Leipzig. These had Sack's name on them, and must have been passed off as being of their manufacture. A somewhat similar engine, dubbed a 'New Zealand traction engine' was built for John Chambers, the company's New Zealand agent. A series of large traction engines for direct traction ploughing, i.e. to haul the implement in the same way as a modern tractor, were built for service in North Africa, the Middle East, and India.

Besides these export ploughing tractions the Works also made a series of 8 and 10 NHP straw-burning traction engines. Many of these were for use in North Africa or South America. The last straw-burners to be made were a trio (Works Nos.35067, 35068, and 35069) despatched to Argentina in 1927, all of which were of 80 BHP. Mostly for their French and North African agents, Th. Pilter et Cie of Paris and Bordeaux, the firm made a series of single speed, single cylinder light traction engines of 4 and 5 NHP. known as Continental traction engines. These appeared between 1911 and 1914.

Between 1923 and 1927 the company also made a series of very simple 4 and 5 NHP single cylinder engines with chain drive for the company's agent Ed. Zehder of Riga, in the then newly established republic of Estonia. These were a reversion to the idea of the self-moving portable. In 1992 a visitor to Estonia found and photographed one more or less intact.

Below: *One of the Aveling type traction engines built by Richard Garrett & Sons under licence, early 1860's*

Above:The self-moving portable of the 1870's driven by the annular gears on each rear wheel.
Below: The only known illustration of one of the cable ploughing engines built for Rudolph Sack .

Above: *An 8 NHP single cylinder traction engine (No.25858 of 1906) owned by G.F.Townsend of Exning, here hauling bagged wheat. Unusually it had motion covers, as in a road locomotive, but was otherwise a straightforward traction engine.*

Below: *A 6NHP compound traction engine(No.30917 of 1912) for direct ploughing in N.Africa, sold through Th.Pilter, the French agent.*

The prototype Suffolk Punch *tractor (No.32974) at work on Strutt & Parker's farms on Foulness Island, 1916*

STEAM TRACTORS

The class of engine known as *steam tractors* was built for management by one man and intended mainly for road haulage, though some were used for agricultural purposes. First authorised in 1896, along with motor cars, tractors were not begun at Leiston until No.25399, a 3 NHP single cylindered machine was built in the summer of 1905, to be followed early the next year by a 4 NHP version. It was, however, with the advent of the 4 NHP compound tractor in May, 1907, that the firm made an indelible mark upon the tractor market. This popular tractor was in production for just over twenty years and numerous examples survive, one of which is housed in the Long Shop Museum collection. Some examples were equipped with superheaters and a limited number with piston valves, but the majority had slide valves and ran on saturated steam.

In 1917 a lightweight steam tractor, dubbed *The Suffolk Punch*, with a reversed boiler and the driving position at the front was produced for direct traction ploughing, but although it worked well enough, lighter and less bulky petrol and paraffin tractors were already on the scene and it was too late to achieve useful sales, only eight being sold. One example, Works No.33180, is included in the Long Shop collection. When new it was bought by John Goddard, a prominent Tunstall farmer, later being owned by Chris Lambert of Horsmonden, Kent, who had some claim to having been the originator of engine preservation.

In 1930 a 6-wheeled steam tractor on solid rubber tyres was devised, based upon the components of the Garrett undertype wagons, wholly enclosed in bodywork, but only three were made.

Above: *No.3 tractor and thresher by the Friends' Meeting House, Waterloo Avenue, Leiston, 1905.*

Below: *No.4 compound tractor No.27886 (1909) owned by Noah Etheridge (in Stetson hat) at Blythburgh Hall.*

Above: *No.4 compound tractor No.32740 (1915) hauling a boiler from Silvertown to the Royal Laundry, Brentwood, 1921. Note the Tangent wooden wheels and the rubber blocks to the rear tyres.* [Photo: F.D.Simpson]

Below: *The final phase of steam tractor building. No.34787 (1927) in show finish for the Norfolk Show, posed in Carr Avenue, Leiston.*

Forrest's 8 NHP. showman's road loco, No.25814 (see below).

ROAD LOCOMOTIVES

The road locomotive is a traction engine designed specially for road haulage, with the engine work covered at the sides, frequently provided with a roof, often with three road speeds in the gearing as opposed to two in most traction engines, made with larger bearing surfaces and strengthened in the axle and cross shafts. Garretts did not set out to be makers of road locos but nevertheless made a number of them, commencing in July, 1903, with No.24369, an 8 NHP engine for Mauritius, followed by No.24429, ordered by Keep Bros. of Birmingham but actually exported by them to New Zealand, and by Nos.24551 and 24552 which went to South Africa. A fifth built in the same batch had a chequered early history, but in spring, 1907, went to Henry Forrest, the Forest Gate (London) showman, later based at Dartford. When delivered it carried a plate saying '12 Tons' but the actual weight with dynamo at the front and twisted brass, and a full load of coal and water was nearer 20 tons. Named *Empress of Japan* and painted dark green with yellow wheels it became a familiar sight on London area fairgrounds until it was scrapped about 1930.

In 1908, the building of a series of 6 NHP road locomotives was begun in response to an enquiry from Lalonde Brothers & Parham of Weston-super-Mare for a fast road engine for furniture removal work. Lalondes and Garretts fell out over the result and nearly went to law, but a further five were built for other customers, including three showmen. The last (No.27946) went to John Harkness & Co. of Belfast who called it *Vera* and it survives in preservation.

Engines for showmen were very striking, having a roof over the whole length of the engine supported on columns encased in 'barley-sugar' brass, and, at the front of the smokebox, a bracket carrying a large dynamo to be driven by a belt from the flywheel to generate light when stationary on a fairground.

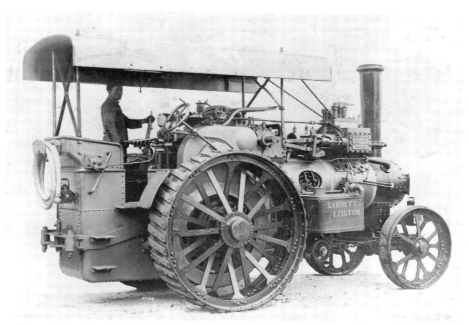

Above: 6 NHP. Road loco with the engine cover removed to show the engine work.

Below: 8 NHP. Road loco for South Africa, 1904, at the corner of Waterloo Avenue
and Station Road, Leiston

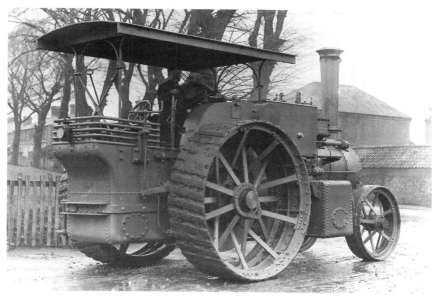

15 ton Roller No.24468 (1903) for Belfast.

STEAM ROLLERS

Throughout the period of their common existence the firms of Richard Garrett & Sons Ltd. and Aveling & Porter Ltd. lived in a *modus vivendi* worked out informally by the heads of the owning families, avoiding treading on each other's toes, so to speak. Victor Garrett told me his father, Frank Garrett, had once said to him that as Avelings had done most to develop the steam roller they should enjoy the biggest share of the sales. Nevertheless, Leiston Works did build steam rollers, though mainly for export. One worked in Japan, many in India and Burma, whilst they were seen all over Europe, especially Germany; the Caribbean area; and Central and South America.

The first was No.21411, based on a 6 NHP single cylindered traction engine and finished in May, 1898. This made a 10 ton (nominal) roller and was sent to Burn & Co. Ltd. who were agents in Howrah near Calcutta and would have sold it on to an Indian municipality. By 1902 the range had been extended to cover 15 tonners, the first of which (No.23607) went to A.Henninger & Co. of Darmstadt, Germany. This was unusual in having the tyres of the rear rollers conical, i.e. 1" less in diameter on the inner edge than on the outer. The biggest roller made weighed 18 tons (No.23729) and was built for the German firm of Ruthemeyer of Soest, later to build rollers in their own works, and had their name on the valve chest covers where normally the Garrett nameplate would have been. The extra weight was achieved by thickening the metal in the rims of the rolls.

By contrast the smallest roller built was No.30268 (1912) for the Ministry of Public Works in Buenos Aires. Based on the No.3 tractor this roller had a nominal weight of 4 tons, but the front and rear rolls were made with steel plates in lieu of spokes, turning them into tanks that could be filled with water to increase the weight when required.

A range of so-called *light* rollers was built around the engine work and boiler designs of the No.3 and No.4 tractors, both single cylindered and compound, and the heavy range was also altered to include compound cylinders. Most went abroad but a few were for home use. For instance, Belfast Corporation had a 15-tonner in 1903, and Fairclough, the Clacton contractor, had several Garrett rollers. However, No.35131 (1928), the last roller to be made, was exported to Arabia.

Above: *A 10 ton single cylinder roller with Bomford scarifier at the rear.*

Below: 'Light' *type 10 ton compound roller (No.34706 - 1925) built for Fairclough of Clacton, and, when photographed, owned by Gray of Hadleigh.*   [Photo: R.G.Pratt]

Above: *4 ton single cylinder roller (No. 30268 - 1912) supplied to the Ministry of Public Works, Buenos Aires. It had water ballasted rolls, and was based on the No.3 tractor.*

Below: *The first steam wagon built at Leiston (No.25065 of 1904)*
       [from a drawing by J.C.Butler]

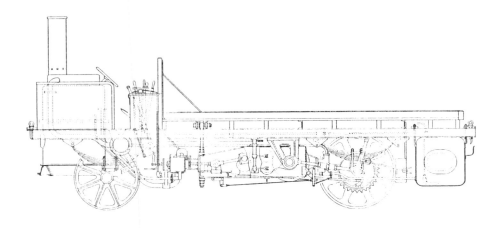

5 ton Overtype wagon No.31226 (1913), with superheater (see the square top to the smokebox below the chimney) in the Old Market, Beccles, Suffolk, with a load of Whitbread's beer. The Bear & Bells *inn is in the background.*

STEAM WAGONS

The company were not pioneers in the building of steam wagons and did not begin until 1904 when an experimental undertype was made. This was not successful and was dismantled, but it was followed by a pair of modified design exported to South America in 1908.

Attention was then turned to building 5-ton overtype wagons, the first of which (No.27720) was completed in July, 1909. A 3-tonner was introduced in 1912, on which solid rubber tyres were standard, and these subsequently were used on many of the later 5-tonners. Until 1912 slide valves were used in the 5-tonners to control the steam admission and exhaust, and these continued to be supplied to order, but piston valves became standard for both 3 and 5-tonners, as also did the installation of a smokebox superheater although many examples were supplied without it. Most wagons had flat or sided non-tipping bodies but tippers were available with hand or power operated gear, and some interesting special bodies were made, as well as a few vans. A few 4-tonners were made, based on a modified 3-ton chassis. Very few 3-tonners were made after 1918, but the manufacture of 5-tonners went on until 1924, and one example was sold in 1926.

In 1917 an experimental wagon was made in which the boiler was reversed, to run with the firebox leading, and the driver and mate were placed at the very front. This had many parts in common with the *Suffolk Punch* tractor already referred to, but the design was not repeated, though it gave the driver a much improved view of the road ahead. Eventually in 1926 an entirely new and much more modern design of 6-ton overtype wagon was launched of which a batch of eight was built but sales were disappointing and it was dropped from production.

Above: *3-tonner No.31130 (1912) fitted with rubber tyres on wooden wheels, in Markham Street, Nottingham.*

Below: *No.32865 (1916), a late type superheated 5-tonner, at the corner of Cross Street and Haylings Road, Leiston.*

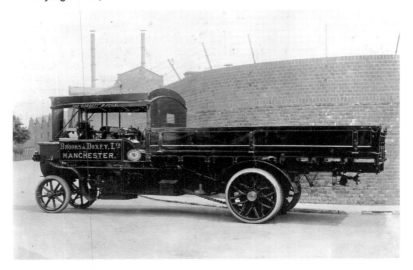

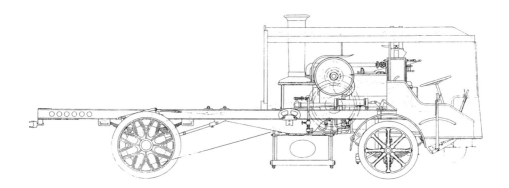

Above: *The XL or* Suffolk Punch *wagon (No.32952 of 1916) was an innovative attempt to solve the problem of the driver's forward vision on overtype wagons by reversing the boiler and putting the driver at the front. It was, however, very extravagant with fuel and water.*
[Drawing by J.C.Butler]

Overtype wagons were robust and relatively easy to drive and maintain, but the locomotive type boiler took up a higher proportion of available chassis length than did the vertical boiler of an undertype, placing them at a disadvantage in the eyes of potential buyers, compared with the undertype. Moreover the market in all types of steam wagon was suffering from the advance of motor lorries.

The making of undertype wagons was recommenced in 1922 when 4-wheeled wagons on solid rubber tyres for loads of 4, 6, or 8 tons were offered. At first engines with piston valves were used, but in 1928 a new design of engine using cam-operated poppet valves (as in a motor vehicle) was introduced. In the same year the company began to build 6-wheeled undertype wagons, then a revolutionary new concept. At first these sold well but problems developed with the superheaters and with the front stub axles, and sales tailed off badly in the late summer of 1930, never to recover, only ten being sold thereafter.

All the undertype wagons were on solid rubber tyres except 4-wheeler No.35473 and 6-wheelers Nos.35469 and 35475, finished right at the end of production in late 1931, which were carried on pneumatic tyres.

Above: *8 ton undertype wagon (with piston valved engine and earliest form of cab) complete with trailer at Station Works, Leiston. It was No.34751 (1925). In emerald green, lettered in gold, it must have been a handsome outfit. Although it had a fixed body, the tank was behind the cab, as in a tipper, possibly to increase ground clearances.*

Below: *The end of a line. 6-wheeler No.35478 left the Works in November, 1931, the last wagon made at Leiston. In 1941 it went to Len and Wilf Cole at the Central Motor & Haulage Co. Leeds, who used it until 1947.*

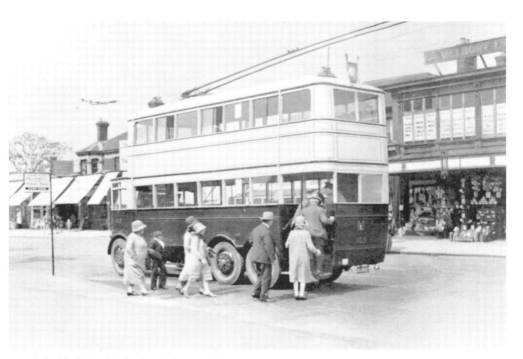

A double decked trolley bus in Southend-on-Sea. The design was made uncompetitive by AEC deciding to lower the rear platform level of their trolley buses to make boarding and alighting easier.

ELECTRIC and MOTOR VEHICLES

Frank Garrett (Junior) was ahead of his time in believing in the electric Vehicle. The first battery electric lorry was a 3½-tonner made in late 1916, but wartime restrictions prevented serious production until 1919 when a series of chain-driven electrics for loads ranging from 1½ to 5 tons was commenced.

In late 1925 work was begun on the design of a 30-seater single decked trolley bus, the first of which went to Ipswich Corporation in Spring, 1926. Most of those sold went to municipal undertakings for tramway replacement. Apart from Ipswich customers included Bradford, Grimsby, West Hartlepool, and St.Helens municipalities, and the company owned Mexborough and Swinton Tramways. Eight were exported to Denmark and six to Peru. In 1928 the range was widened to include a 60-seat 6-wheeled double-decker of which four were sold to Doncaster and six to Southend-on-Sea. The last trolley bus was sold in 1931.

Meanwhile in 1927 a large order for battery refuse collectors had been won from Glasgow Corporation by a very original and ingenious design which continued in production for over ten years. The original order was for solid tyred vehicles, but later ones were on pneumatics, and earlier examples were converted from solids to pneumatics after some years in service. Apart from these production of electrics ceased before 1932.

Leiston Works produced no significant numbers of internal combustion lorries. In 1927 the Caledon Motor Company of Glasgow ceased to trade and Garretts bought the goodwill and stock in trade but the designs were already obsolescent. Three Caledons were made at Leiston, only one of which was sold. Next, two diesel lorries were made by putting McLaren Benz diesel engines into the chassis and bodywork of the 4 and 6-wheeled steam wagons - another non-success! Finally prototypes were built of lorries of up-to-date design, with fully enclosed cabs and using, respectively, a Blackstone diesel engine and a Meadows petrol engine. Work on these was abandoned when the original firm ceased in 1932. One refuse collection vehicle using a Blackstone engine was built for Glasgow Corporation in 1931.

Fourteen diesel engined tractors were made between 1929 and 1934 using, variously, Blackstone; Aveling & Porter; and Gardner engines, followed by five interesting but commercially unsuccessful crawler tractors with front controls; four industrial tractors for export; and nearly four hundred tractors for peat harvesting in Eire and the North of Scotland. The last of these was built in 1959, and a large amount of peat-harvesting machinery was made for use with them.

Below: *The GTZ battery electric refuse collection vehicle for Glasgow Corporation. The refuse collected was burned under boilers that provided steam for generators, the electricity from which charged the batteries of the lorries. Glasgow had a fleet of 64 between 1927 and 1937, the last eleven on pneumatics, to which the earlier ones were also converted.*

OTHER PRODUCTS & ACTIVITIES

Garretts were always ready to undertake any general engineering tasks within the capacity of the Works. As they had a fully equipped iron and non-ferrous metal foundry and a large boiler shop as well as comprehensive machining facilities and a woodworking department this capacity was broad. Thus as long ago as the 1870's they made a set of plant for the manufacture of beet sugar in Hungary, and equipment for Robert Tooth, the Australian manufacturer of cane sugar and meat extract. A little earlier they had had general ironmongers' shops at Saxmundham, Leiston, and Yoxford. They built plant for the malting at Snape owned by Newson Garrett (brother of Richard III), and a boiler for one of his steam barges.

Items ancillary to their main products were made in considerable numbers. Thus, in this century, they made nearly 400 straw choppers; 500 clover hullers; nearly 2000 mealie and maize shellers of all types; just on 300 trailers and traction wagons; 117 sleeping vans; 400 hayloaders; and 1000 plough beams.

For a long period until the opening, in 1910, of the works of the Leiston Gas Company (much of the initiative and funds for which came from the Garretts) they supplied the Works and town from their private gas works in Haylings Road, part of which is still known to old inhabitants as Gas Hill. Again, until the Leiston Urban District Council built a waterworks in 1901/02 the artesian well at the Garrett Works provided one of the very few unsuspect sources of drinking water in the area.

In both world wars they made artillery shells and built lathes for their manufacture. In the 1914/18 war they built 2324 military wagons and carts, and also aeroplanes (the FE2/B) and in the second made guns. In 1924 much of the equipment for the Never-Stop Railway at the Wembley Exhibition was made at Leiston, and other products in the latter 20's included bakers' ovens, sausage machines, cake and dough mixers, freezers, and petrol and oil pumps. In the 30's and onwards they made machine tools, whilst in the 1960's and 70's they manufactured machines for dry cleaning; for making cardboard boxes; and for plastics moulding. Other contracts included electrical work such as assembling radio sets, and making fires, kettles, and irons. At one point they also made a range of toys. The firm's readiness to help was legendary. At different times they put right a steam car belonging to Stuart Ogilvie of Sizewell, repaired a mower for a townsman, and replated some candlesticks for a West Country parson. When the Works closed it was, to many, like the death of a friend.

CONSTITUENT COMPANIES of A.G.E.

Aveling & Porter Ltd. Rochester.
Richard Garrett & Sons Ltd. Leiston.
James & Frederick Howard Ltd. Bedford.
E.H.Bentall & Co. Ltd. Heybridge, Maldon, Essex.
Blackstone & Co. Ltd. Stamford.
Clarke's Crank & Forge Co. Ltd. Lincoln.
L.R.Knapp & Co. Ltd. Clanfield, Oxon.
E.R. & F. Turner Ltd. Ipswich.
Bull Motors Ltd. Stowmarket.
Charles Burrell & Sons Ltd. Thetford.
Davey Paxman & Co. Ltd. Colchester.
Peter Brotherhood Ltd. Peterborough.

TOTALS OF STEAM ENGINES MADE

Production records are not wholly complete, but it is estimated that some 22500 steam engines of all types were made. These included:

Traction engines, ploughing engines, and self-moving portables	c.525
Steam tractors	560
Road locomotives	11
Steam rollers	380
Overtype steam wagons	689
Undertype steam wagons	306

Portables and fixed engines made up the balance - i.e. approx. 20 000

GARRETT ARTEFACTS & ARCHIVES

The Long Shop Museum, Leiston, Suffolk IP16 4ES.
Erected by the third Richard Garrett in 1853 in which to build his portable steam engines on a logical work-flow principle this impressive galleried building was soon outgrown by the rapidly expanding scale of manufacture but survived as an ordinary workshop. When work ceased at the Town Works in 1978 it passed to Trustees, who have since restored and opened it as a museum housing Garrett machines and memorabilia. The Long Shop is open daily from Easter to the end of September, and is well worth a visit. Telephone: 0728 832189

Suffolk County Council Records Office, Gatacre Road, Ipswich IP1 2LQ.
The archives, which may be inspected by members of the public, include a huge collection of documents and drawings relating both to the technical and the commercial aspects of Leiston Works. Open from 9 a.m. to 5 p.m. Monday to Thursday, 9 a.m. to 4 p.m. Friday, 9 a.m. to 1 p.m. and 2 p.m to 5 p.m Saturday.   Telephone: 0473 230000

East Anglia Transport Museum, Carlton Colville, Lowestoft NR33 8BL
Among its impressive collection of passenger transport vehicles - trams, trolley buses, and motor buses - is a Garrett single decked trolley bus from the batch supplied to NESA in Copenhagen (temporarily on a visit to Copenhagen until 1996). Open every Sunday and Bank Holiday from May to September, plus Saturdays June to September, and other weekdays in August only.
Telephone: 0502 518459.

OTHER BOOKS ON GARRETTS

During its life the Works and its products received frequent mention in the trade and engineering press, but so far as is known the following are the only books devoted solely to the firm or its products:

1964	R.A.Whitehead	Garretts of Leiston	Percival Marshall	London
1978	R.A.Whitehead	Garrett 200	Transport Bookman	London
1994	R.A.Whitehead	Garrett Diesel Tractors	RAWhitehead & Ptnrs	Tonbridge

GLOSSARY

Topographical
Town Works: The older of the firm's two works, bounded by Main Street, High Street, Cross Street, and Haylings Road.

Station Works: The more modern works bounded by Waterloo Avenue, Station road, and Leiston railway station.

Technical
a] Types of engine
i] *Agricultural (or general purpose engines).* The general run of traction engines, intended for threshing, sawing, and other farm or forestry purposes, together with a limited use for road haulage.

ii] *Road locomotives.* Traction engines intended primarily for heavy haulage, having larger bearings, stronger gears, and the engine covered by motion plates (to avoid frightening horses).

iii] *Tractors.* Light road locomotives capable of being managed by one man. First authorised in 1896, one man management was limited to tractors weighing 3 tons or less, but was extended to 5-tonners in 1904.

iv] *Rollers.* Essentially traction engines or tractors with broad smooth wheels, the front ones running edge to edge in a fork instead of at opposite ends of the axle.

v] *Wagons.* Steam vehicles carrying their load upon their own frame as opposed to hauling it. Some had locomotive type boilers, as in a traction engine, but others had vertical boilers (i.e. boilers in which the central axis of the cylindrical boiler was vertical). Garrett wagons with locomotive boilers were overtypes (i.e. the engine was on top of the boiler), and those with vertical boilers were undertypes(with the engine under the chassis).

vi] *Portables.* Agricultural steam engines on wheels but without means of self-propulsion. Self-moving portables were made capable of limited self-propulsion by a chain coupling the engine to a road wheel, but were lighter, and generally cruder, than an agricultural traction engine.

b] Construction of Engines
Boilers. Most boilers in Garrett engines were what is known as 'locomotive' type i.e. the cylindrical main body had a horizontal axis with the firebox projecting below it at one end and smoke tubes to conduct the products of combustion through the cylindrical part of the boiler. A longitudinal section of such a boiler is given overleaf. Undertype wagons, as noted above, had 'vertical' boilers in which the cylindrical shell was set vertically, and the firebox was within it. Such boilers were, in effect, a water jacket around a furnace with tubes, filled with boiler water, criss-crossing the furnace to increase the heating surface.

Cylinders. The thermal efficiency of the engine is represented by the 'pressure drop' i.e. the difference between the pressure of the steam entering the engine and that of the exhaust to atmosphere, less, of course, losses due to friction, radiation, and condensation - the greater the difference between the two, the greater the efficiency. The difference may be increased by 'cut-off' - stopping live steam entering the cylinder before it has completed its stroke and thus allowing expansion of the steam to work on the piston. Thermal efficiency may also be enhanced by using the steam in two stages, first in a high pressure cylinder and then, after it has left there, by using it again in a large low pressure cylinder. This is the compound system. An engine may, however, have two high pressure cylinders, exhausting independently to atmosphere. Such engines are described as 'double cylinder' and the Garrett undertype wagons were arranged in this way, except for the pioneer examples made in 1904/08, which were compound.

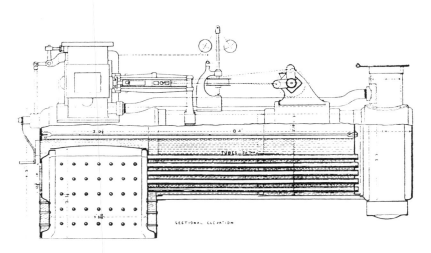

Longitudinal section of a locomotive type boiler - that of the first Garrett compound portable, 1880.

c] Management of steam

The steam boiled off from water, whatever the pressure, is known as saturated steam, but once it has reached this point it becomes, of course, a gas, and can, with suitable treatment, be made much hotter than the boiling point of the water in the boiler. This process is known as 'superheating' and can be continued to the point where the pipes conveying the steam are hot enough to glow in the dark. Heating to this degree, one must hasten to say, did not occur in any of the superheaters fitted to Garrett engines which were smokebox (as opposed to smoke-tube) type, and imparted a very modest amount of superheat. These produced an appreciable economy of fuel and water in engines working steadily hour after hour, such as a portable or fixed engine driving a dynamo or a pump, though it was secured by additional initial cost and higher day to day attention coupled with higher maintenance cost. Superheating was helpful in keeping the steam dry in the long pipe from the boiler to engine on an undertype wagon, but of marginal value on most other steam vehicles. Most Garrett superheaters took the form of two cast steel headers, linked by loops of solid drawn steel tubes, over which the hot flue gases passed, one header receiving saturated steam from the boiler and the other delivering the steam, superheated by its passage through the coils, to the engine.

d] Road gearing

Unlike railway steam locomotives which are virtually all direct drive, road steam engines were arranged so that by the interpolation of gears and/or a driving chain the engine speed of rotation was more rapid than that of the road wheels. Some were fitted only with a single speed, but most had two speeds, and a more limited number, mostly, but not invariably, road locomotives and steam wagons, had three speeds.

e] Threshing machines.

Threshing machines were a very important part of the Garrett output for many years up to the outbreak of war in 1914. In the twelve years from 1903 to 1914 they built 3935 threshers, but because of the changed circumstances in Europe, the following decade saw an output of only 310, an important contribution to the firm's decline. It would be out of place here to embark on a detailed discussion of the design and attributes of threshing machines, but a longitudinal sectional diagram is printed overleaf of a *Mammoth* machine (the largest made by Garretts), giving the names of the various major components and their respective functions.

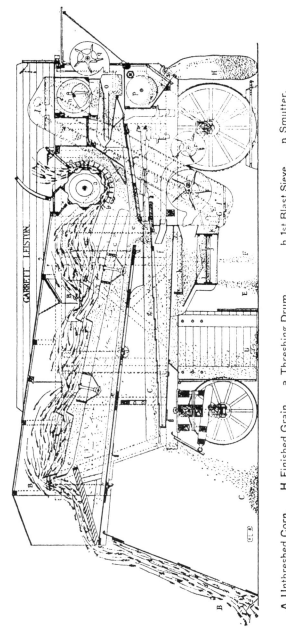

GARRETT LEISTON

A Unthreshed Corn. H Finished Grain.

B Straw.
C Cavings.
D Chaff.
E Chobs.
F Dust.
G Threshed Corn.

a Threshing Drum.
b Concave.
c Shakers.
d 2nd Shaking Apparatus.
e Top Screen.
f Bottom Screen.
g Caving Sieve.

h 1st Blast Sieve.
i Chob Sieve.
j Dust Sieve.
k Corn Spout to
    Elevator.
l Corn Elevator.
m 1st Fan.

n Smutter.
o Riddlebox.
p Revolving Screen.
q 2nd Fan.
r 3rd Fan.
s Corn Spouts.

31

A No.4 compound tractor (No.32653 built in 1915) delivered to E.& A.Shadrack, the East Ham, London, coal merchants, painted green with red wheels. Despite the war being on it was finished in Royal Show finish. It was sold a year later to John Mowlem & Co., the London builders who ran it until 1929.